THE STORY BEHIND

GOLD

Elizabeth Raum

www.raintreepublishers.co.uk
Visit our website to find out more information about Raintree books.

To order:
☏ Phone 0845 6044371
🖹 Fax +44 (0) 1865 312263
✉ Email myorders@capstonepub.co.uk

Customers from outside the UK please telephone +44 1865 312262

Edited by Louise Galpine, Megan Cotugno, and Diyan Leake
Designed by Philippa Jenkins and Artistix
Original illustrations © Capstone Global Library Ltd
Illustrated by Gary Slater/Specs Art
Picture research by Mica Brancic and Elaine Willis
Originated by Modern Age Repro House Ltd
Printed and bound in China by CTPS

ISBN 978 0 431114 86 6 (hardback)
13 12 11 10 09
10 9 8 7 6 5 4 3 2 1

ISBN 978 0 431115 00 9 (paperback)
14 13 12 11 10
10 9 8 7 6 5 4 3 2 1

British Library Cataloguing in Publication Data
Raum, Elizabeth
The story behind gold. – (True stories)
553.4'1
A full catalogue record for this book is available from the British Library.

Acknowledgements
We would like to thank the following for permission to reproduce photographs: © 2008 Photolibrary.com pp. 10 (North Wind Pictures), 19 (Robert Harding Travel/Rod Porteous), 21 (SGM SGM); © akg-images p. 6; AP/PA Photos p. 26 (© Mark J. Terrill); Bridgeman Art Library p. 24 (© Boltin Picture Library/Museo del Oro, Bogota, Colombia); Corbis pp. 4 (© Steve Starr), 7 (© The Gallery Collection), 11 (© Bettmann), 12 (Dallas Morning News/© Tom Fox), 13 (© Evan Collis), 14 (© Reuters/Laszlo Balogh), 16 (© Bettmann), 17 (© Charles O'Rear), 18 (© Bettmann), 20 (© Roger Ressmeyer), 25 (© Reuters/Andy Newman), 27 (Atlantide Phototravel/© Massimo Borchi); Getty Images pp. iii (PhotoDisc/© 3 Squared Studios), 9 (© Kean Collection/Hulton Archive); Mary Evans Picture Library p. 22 (© Estate of Arthur Rackham); The Art Archive p. 8 (Archaeological Museum Lima/© Mireille Vautier).

Cover photograph of gold bars reproduced with permission of © Photolibrary Group (SGM SGM).

Every effort has been made to contact copyright holders of any material reproduced in this book. Any omissions will be rectified in subsequent printings if notice is given to the publisher.

All the Internet addresses (URLs) given in this book were valid at the time of going to press. However, due to the dynamic nature of the Internet, some addresses may have changed, or sites may have changed or ceased to exist since publication. While the author and publisher regret any inconvenience this may cause readers, no responsibility for any such changes can be accepted by either the author or the publisher.

Contents

Some words are shown in bold, **like this**.
You can find out what they mean by looking in the glossary.

The world's greatest treasure

▲ **This large gold nugget was found in California, USA in 1993.**

Gold is the world's greatest treasure. People use it as money and wear it as jewellery. People and countries with lots of gold are considered rich and powerful. That is why **monarchs** (kings and queens) wear golden crowns and important buildings have golden domes.

Gold is valuable because it is rare. Experts say that the total amount of gold **mined** throughout history would fit into 60 lorries. Gold is a soft, yellow metal. It is found throughout Earth in tiny amounts mixed with other rocks and **minerals**.

Gold is an **element**. This means it cannot be broken down into anything else. Gold does not change. Copper turns green over time. Silver turns black. Iron rusts. But gold stays bright and shiny even after years of use. Even gold buried underground or underwater does not lose its value.

Carats

The purity of gold is measured in units called carats (ct). Pure gold is 24ct gold. Each country sets its own standard for gold jewellery. The United Kingdom uses 9ct gold as the standard. In Germany gold jewellery must be at least 8ct. In Italy and France, gold jewellery must be at least 18ct. In the United States, most jewellery is 14ct.

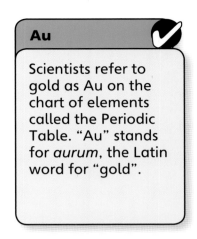

Au ✔

Scientists refer to gold as Au on the chart of elements called the Periodic Table. "Au" stands for *aurum*, the Latin word for "gold".

▼ **This map shows where gold has been found around the world.**

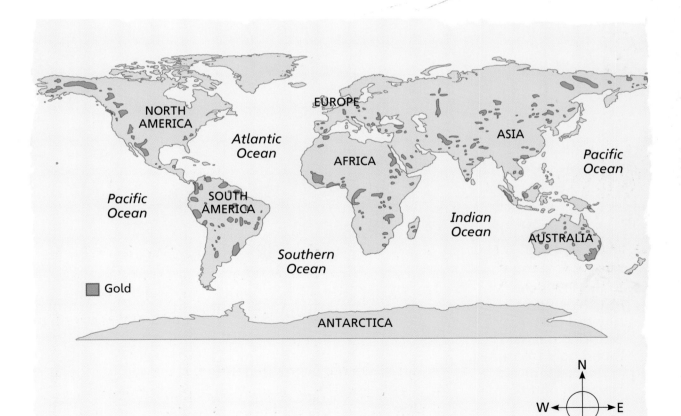

NORTH AMERICA

Atlantic Ocean

EUROPE

ASIA

Pacific Ocean

AFRICA

Pacific Ocean

SOUTH AMERICA

Indian Ocean

AUSTRALIA

Southern Ocean

■ Gold

ANTARCTICA

N
W ← → E
S

A short history of gold

▲ **In the 1920s the British explorer Howard Carter (wearing glasses) found gold treasures in the tomb of the Egyptian pharaoh Tutankhamen.**

Ancient peoples used gold as jewellery and decoration. They hammered and melted it into different shapes.

4000 BCE
There are over 100 gold mines in Egypt. Traders seek gold.

4000 BCE   **3000** BCE   **2000** BCE

Egyptian gold

In ancient Egypt, gold belonged only to the **pharaohs** (rulers). They used it as jewellery and decoration. By 4000 **BCE** (about 6,000 years ago), Egypt had over 100 gold **mines** worked by slaves. People from parts of Asia and Africa used gold to trade.

▲ This solid gold mask was found in Tutankhamen's tomb.

Hatshepsut ✔

A woman named Hatshepsut was Egypt's pharaoh from 1470 BCE to 1458 BCE. She painted her face with gold and silver dust. She sent explorers as far south as present-day Zimbabwe (in Africa) in search of gold.

Gold coins

King Croesus of ancient Lydia (in western Asia) issued the first gold coins around 800 BCE. Bankers tested the value of the coins and marked them with a royal stamp. Lydia became a trading centre. Everyone wanted gold coins.

Roman gold

By 150 BCE the leaders of ancient Rome wanted more gold. This would show their power and wealth. They sent Roman soldiers on raids to capture gold. They took slaves to work in Italy's gold mines. Wealthy Romans wore gold jewellery, decorated their homes with gold, and collected gold coins.

Constantine's crown ✔

When Constantine ruled Rome (306–337 CE), he wore a golden crown at all times. He also created a gold coin called a solidus. It remained in use for 700 years.

1460 BCE	**800 BCE**	**150 BCE**	**58 BCE**	**325 CE**
Egyptian pharaoh Hatshepsut seeks gold in southern Africa.	King Croesus makes gold coins in Lydia.	The leaders of ancient Rome send soldiers to capture gold.	Roman leader Julius Caesar takes gold from France.	Roman ruler Constantine issues the solidus.

Riches for monarchs

Gold and jewels became a sign of power and wealth throughout the world. But the **monarchs** of Europe were running out of gold. Where would they find more?

The Americas

The Italian explorer Christopher Columbus provided an answer. Working for the king and queen of Spain, he sailed to the Americas. In 1493 he returned with stories of the gold there. The news encouraged Spanish explorers to set out on more **expeditions**.

In 1502 the Spanish explorer Francisco Pizarro sailed to the Americas to find gold. The Incas of Peru and the Aztecs of Mexico were expert goldsmiths (people who work with gold). In Peru, Pizarro met the Inca emperor Atahualpa. Pizarro saw gold plates, vases, bracelets, and masks. He murdered Atahualpa and carried the Inca gold back to Spain. Until the 1800s, most of the world's gold would continue to come from South America.

► Inca people, who lived in what is now Peru, created this solid gold figure of a llama.

1492	1533
Italian explorer Christopher Columbus finds gold in the Americas.	Spanish explorer Francisco Pizarro murders Inca emperor Atahualpa for Inca gold.

◀ In this drawing, a Spanish member of Pizarro's expedition is presenting a cross to the Inca emperor Atahualpa in 1532. Later Pizarro murdered the emperor for his gold.

1577–79

English explorer Sir Francis Drake captures Spanish gold.

▲ California gold **miners** used picks and shovels to dig for gold and pans to sift for gold.

California Gold Rush

In the 1800s, new gold discoveries excited people around the world.

On 24 January 1848, a US builder called James Marshall discovered gold at Sutter's Mill in California, USA. Thousands of people rushed to California. The journey was dangerous, and many never arrived.

In 1849 alone, 80,000 people reached California. They found gold by using pans in streams and rivers or by digging near by. Some struck it rich, but most left with nothing. More than $200 million in gold was **mined** during the California Gold Rush.

1848
Gold is discovered in California.

1851
Gold is discovered in New South Wales, Australia.

1854
Gold is discovered in British Columbia, Canada.

1859
Gold is discovered in Nevada, USA.

1840   1850   1860

Other gold rushes

From 1852 to 1886, gold was discovered in other US states including Nevada, Colorado, Montana, and South Dakota. Gold was also discovered in Canada. In 1897 the Klondike Gold Rush spread from Canada to Alaska. Bad weather and rough travel prevented many gold seekers from reaching the goldfields there.

In 1852, 1864, and 1893, gold hunters rushed to New Zealand and Australia for gold. The last great gold rush took place in South Africa in 1886.

▼ These miners in Alaska are weighing the gold they found during the winter of 1897.

1886
Gold is discovered in South Africa.

1897
The Klondike Gold Rush spreads to Alaska.

1880   1890   1900

Finding, mining, and refining gold

▲ These miners
in South Africa
are working
2.8 kilometres
(1.75 miles) below
Earth's surface.

Minerals or rocks that contain gold and other metals are called **ores**. Some ores lie on the surface of Earth. Others are buried deep in the ground.

Finding gold

Earth scientists, called geologists, test ore to see if it contains gold. Most gold is mixed with the metals copper, lead, and zinc. If the ore is rich in minerals, geologists decide how to **mine** it.

Mining

Today, **lode mining** (also called vein mining) is the most common way to mine gold. To reach the ore, **miners** dig deep passages called shafts. Dust and gases that collect in the mine are harmful for miners to breathe. Huge fans bring fresh air into large underground mines. Underground mines are costly to dig. This adds to the price of gold.

Other mines called **open pit mines**, or surface mines, are dug from the surface. Layers of earth are scraped away to make a deep pit. Miners remove the gold from the ore as the mine is dug. This is faster, easier, and cheaper than underground mining.

▼ An open pit gold mine like this one in Australia removes layers of earth to find gold.

▲ These fish were killed when poison from a gold mine leaked into a river in Romania in 2000.

Fighting over gold

Some people do not want a gold mine close to where they live. Communities must make difficult decisions when gold is discovered near by. People living near the border of Costa Rica and Nicaragua did not want an open pit mine near their homes. People in Alaska were upset about plans to dig a mine there, too.

What's the problem?

These people feared that open pit mining would damage the environment. It puts deadly chemicals and minerals into the water. Cyanide, a chemical used to separate the gold from the other metals, may run into the water supply. It is poison and can kill plants, flowers, and animals that use the water. Open pit mining also removes trees. It leaves deep pits in the earth where nothing grows.

Mining companies disagree

Mining companies claim that everyone will benefit from the mines. Mining brings hundreds of jobs to an area. The companies promise to protect the land and water by building large **dams** to keep mining waste away from rivers and streams. They also promise to fill in the land and to replant trees.

Ghana ✔

In 2001, when waste from a gold mine in Ghana (in Africa) washed into the Asuman River, hundreds of fish, crabs, and birds died. People could not drink the water or sell their crops. As a result, they had to move away.

▼ **An open pit mine includes the mine itself. It also includes several dumps for waste rock. There is also a pond that is used to separate the gold from other metals.**

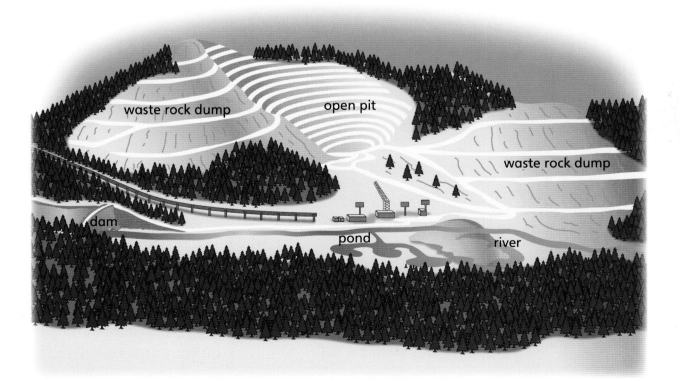

waste rock dump · open pit · waste rock dump · dam · pond · river

▲ These miners are using a rocker to separate gold from river dirt and sand.

Placer mining

Placer mining is different from lode or open pit mining. It is used when gold has been washed out of mountains into rivers and streams. The simplest method is to swirl the sand and gravel in a pan of water. The water carries the sand and gravel away, leaving the heavier gold behind. Miners also use a box called a rocker to trap particles (tiny pieces) of gold. Water running through the box carries sand and gravel away, leaving gold behind.

Refining

In placer mining, gold is already separated from the surrounding rock. But in lode mining, the gold must be treated to remove rocks or to separate it from other minerals, such as silver or platinum. This is called refining. To refine gold, workers may add chemicals to the ore. They may also use electricity or high heat (a process called smelting) to melt and separate pure gold from the other metals.

Hidden gold

About 9 billion tonnes of gold are located beneath Earth's oceans. There is no simple way to get it out. There is even more gold in space. In 1999 a US spacecraft proved that the **asteroid** Eros is loaded with gold and other precious metals. Scientists think other asteroids may also contain gold. For now, there is no way to mine the gold in space.

◀ Gold is melted and poured into moulds.

Global gold production (in 2007)	
China	11.3%
South Africa	11.1%
United States	10.4%
Australia	10.3%
Indonesia	7.6%
Peru	6.9%
Russia	6.2%
Canada	3.8%
All others	32.9%

Putting gold to work

▲ **These men are keeping watch over gold stored in bars at New York's Federal Reserve Bank. Each bar weighs about 12.2 kilograms (27 pounds).**

For thousands of years, gold has been used as money. Gold coins were common throughout the world at one time. Gold coins were used in Britain as far back as the early 800s.

Gold bars

Today, much of the world's gold is stored as gold bars. Most countries keep a supply of gold bars that they can use to trade with other nations. This gold proves their wealth.

Gold in Asia

In the past, Asian rulers used gold as decoration, not as money. They traded spices, silk, and tea for Europe's gold. Even today, people in countries like India use gold for jewellery and decoration rather than money.

Golden threads ✔

About one-fifth of the decorative gold in the world is used as threads in saris. Saris are long pieces of cloth worn like a dress by women in India.

Gold beneath New York City ✔

About one-third of the world's gold bars are stored in the Federal Reserve Bank in the United States. The gold is stored 24 metres (80 feet) below the streets of New York City. It belongs to many countries, including the United Kingdom and France. They trust the US bank to keep it safe. Each bar is weighed and inspected to make sure it is at least 99.5 per cent pure.

▶ Chinese rulers used gold to decorate buildings such as these temples in Sichuan.

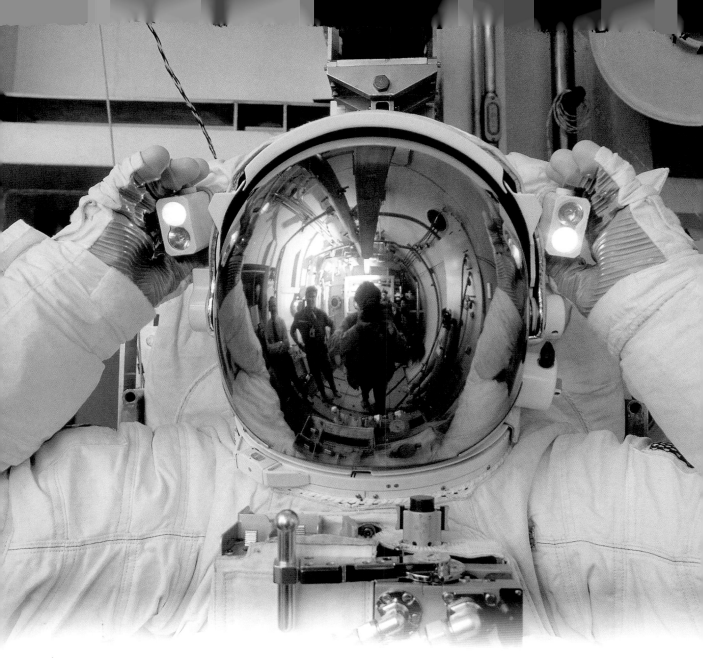

▲ A thin layer of gold
coats the visor of an
astronaut's helmet.
It reflects the sun,
protecting the
astronaut's eyes.

Computer gold

People use gold every day. They use it as money or
jewellery. But they also use it in unexpected ways.

Gold is soft enough to be spun into thin wires.
Like gold itself, gold wire lasts forever. It also
conducts (carries) electricity easily. These qualities
make gold the best choice for computer parts. The
plugs on printers, keyboards, and computer mice
are coated with a thin layer of gold. Gold makes
them last.

◀ Computers work better and last longer when the wires and connections are coated with gold.

Telephones and televisions

Gold is also used in telephones. Gold carries electric signals clearly, making it easier to hear over the phone. Hair-thin gold wires are used in televisions. They pick up television signals clearly. There is also gold on the cables that connect televisions to DVD players, set-top boxes, and cable boxes.

Medicine

Gold is used in medicine because it lasts forever and is safe. Gold has long been used for teeth fillings and caps. Often dentists mix it with other metals such as silver, copper, and zinc. Gold is also used to repair certain eye problems. Doctors use gold to treat some forms of cancer and arthritis, a painful disease of the joints. They may inject little gold pellets into the body. The gold helps the body fight these diseases.

Gold lasers ✔

Doctors use gold instruments during heart surgery. **Lasers** are instruments that use light to help doctors perform surgery. They are coated with gold. This helps the laser focus its beam on the problem area.

Stories and legends

▲ King Midas was horrified when his daughter turned to gold at his touch.

Gold, with its promise of great riches, plays an important role in stories and **legends**. One of the earliest is the story of King Midas.

King Midas

Midas was a real king who lived in what is now Turkey around 700 BCE. He was a good man who wanted to help others. According to legend, Midas invited a stranger into his home and treated him kindly. The Roman god Bacchus was so pleased that he rewarded Midas for his kindness by granting him one wish.

Midas wished that everything he touched would turn to gold. At first, it seemed like a wise idea. But when he tried to eat, Midas's food turned to gold. When he hugged his little daughter, she turned into a golden statue. Midas begged Bacchus to take away the golden touch. Bacchus agreed. The story teaches people not to be too greedy.

Rumpelstiltskin

The German fairy tale of Rumpelstiltskin also warns about the danger of greediness. In this story, a poor man wants to be important. So, he says that his daughter can spin gold from straw. The king orders the girl to do so. She faces one problem after another all because her father wants to be important.

▼ There are many Chinese **proverbs** about gold.

"Gold has a price, but people are priceless."

"Piles of gold are not as good as stores of grain."

"A fair lady's smile is worth more than a thousand ounces of gold."

"A lost inch of gold may be reclaimed, but never a lost inch of time."

"Fierce fire reveals true gold."

"A family with an old person has a living treasure of gold."

"Gold or silver mansions are not as good as one's own thatched house."

"Do not pray for gold and jade and precious things; pray that your children and grandchildren may all be good."

El Dorado

A famous legend about gold is the story of El Dorado. *El Dorado* means "gilded man" in Spanish. The legend told of a South American king who covered himself with gold dust every day. He washed it off at night. The next morning, he covered himself with gold again. In the 1500s and 1600s, Spanish explorers looked for the country of El Dorado. So did the English explorer Sir Walter Raleigh.

But El Dorado did not exist. The story probably began with the Chibcha people, who lived in what is now Colombia. When they chose a new chief, they covered his body with gold dust. When he washed it off, gold flowed into the nearby stream.

▶ **This small sculpture from ancient Colombia shows the ceremony of El Dorado.**

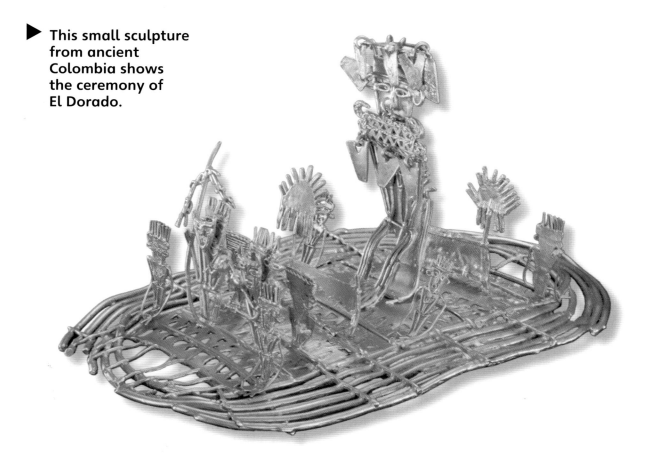

Lost mine

According to another legend, a Mexican family discovered gold in Arizona, USA in the 1840s. On their last trip back to Mexico, the family was attacked and killed by **Apaches**. Many people searched for the family's **mine**. One man said he found it. But he died before he told anyone where it was. People are still searching for the lost mine.

Sunken treasure ✔

According to some reports, there are more than three million shipwrecks on the ocean floor. Not all wrecks contain treasure, but many do. For example, the Spanish ship *Atocha* sank in a hurricane in 1622. It carried £67 million in gold and silver. New ships with robot arms and special cameras help find sunken gold.

◀ This is a photo of David Horan, a lawyer involved in a movement to make new laws about sunken ships. He is showing just some of the gold recovered from the *Atocha*.

Treasure for everyone

Over the years, people have risked their lives to get gold. The ancient Romans waged wars over gold. Spanish explorers crossed stormy seas in search of gold. They destroyed villages for gold. Ordinary people risked their lives to reach the United States, Alaska, or Australia during the gold rushes in the 1800s.

Gold for everyone

Today, people do not have to be rich or take chances to own gold. People use gold in computers, televisions, and telephones. In the Olympic Games, winners earn gold medals. Even some books have pages trimmed in gold. Gold is still rare, but if you know where to look, you can find little bits of gold right in your own home.

▶ **US swimmer Michael Phelps holds up one of the eight gold medals he won in the 2008 Olympics. In competitions, first-place medals are usually gold.**

Gold teeth ✔

Dentists used gold to fix teeth as early as the 7th century **BCE**. They attached fake teeth with gold wires. By the 1500s, dentists made gold fillings. Today, in some parts of Asia, gold teeth show wealth. People may even have gold caps put over healthy teeth.

Gold leaf

Gold leaf is a very thin sheet of gold used for decorating glass, metal, paper, wood, pottery, and cloth. To make gold leaf, pure gold is melted, made into a small block, and then rolled and hammered into very thin squares.

▼ **This worker is applying gold leaf to the spine of a book.**

Timeline
(These dates are often approximations.)

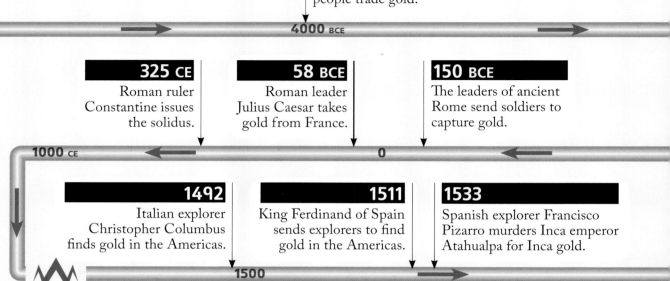

4000 BCE
The Egyptians have over 100 gold **mines**. Ancient people trade gold.

4000 BCE

325 CE
Roman ruler Constantine issues the solidus.

58 BCE
Roman leader Julius Caesar takes gold from France.

150 BCE
The leaders of ancient Rome send soldiers to capture gold.

1000 CE

0

1492
Italian explorer Christopher Columbus finds gold in the Americas.

1511
King Ferdinand of Spain sends explorers to find gold in the Americas.

1533
Spanish explorer Francisco Pizarro murders Inca emperor Atahualpa for Inca gold.

1500

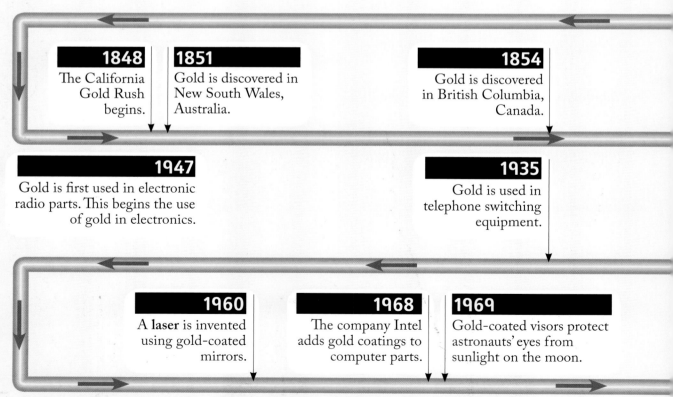

1848
The California Gold Rush begins.

1851
Gold is discovered in New South Wales, Australia.

1854
Gold is discovered in British Columbia, Canada.

1947
Gold is first used in electronic radio parts. This begins the use of gold in electronics.

1935
Gold is used in telephone switching equipment.

1960
A **laser** is invented using gold-coated mirrors.

1968
The company Intel adds gold coatings to computer parts.

1969
Gold-coated visors protect astronauts' eyes from sunlight on the moon.

This symbol shows where there is a change of scale in the timeline, or where a long period of time with no noted events has been left out.

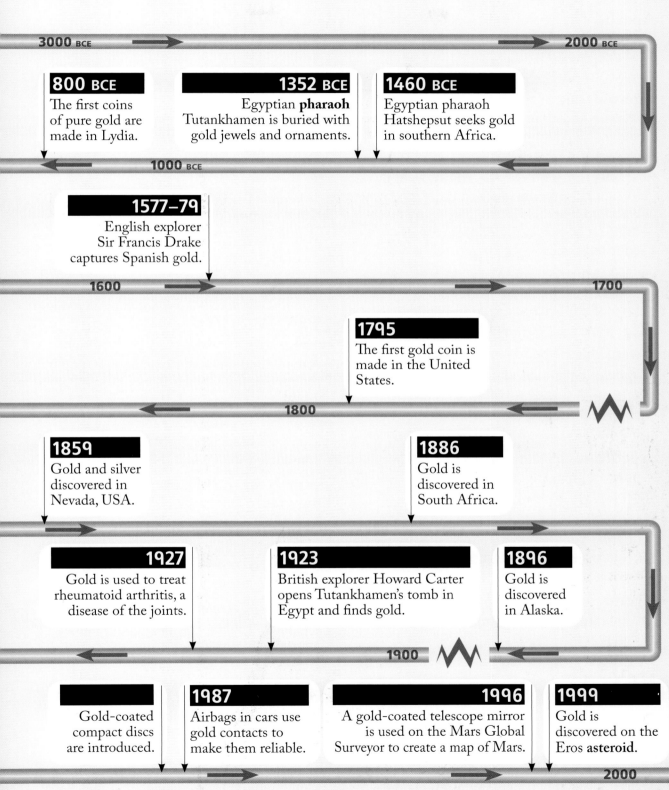

3000 BCE → **2000 BCE**

800 BCE
The first coins of pure gold are made in Lydia.

1352 BCE
Egyptian **pharaoh** Tutankhamen is buried with gold jewels and ornaments.

1460 BCE
Egyptian pharaoh Hatshepsut seeks gold in southern Africa.

1000 BCE

1577–79
English explorer Sir Francis Drake captures Spanish gold.

1600 → **1700**

1795
The first gold coin is made in the United States.

1800

1859
Gold and silver discovered in Nevada, USA.

1886
Gold is discovered in South Africa.

1927
Gold is used to treat rheumatoid arthritis, a disease of the joints.

1923
British explorer Howard Carter opens Tutankhamen's tomb in Egypt and finds gold.

1896
Gold is discovered in Alaska.

1900

Gold-coated compact discs are introduced.

1987
Airbags in cars use gold contacts to make them reliable.

1996
A gold-coated telescope mirror is used on the Mars Global Surveyor to create a map of Mars.

1999
Gold is discovered on the Eros **asteroid**.

2000

Glossary

Apache Native American people who live in the southwestern United States. Today, most Apache people live in Arizona, New Mexico, and Oklahoma.

asteroid one of the many small planets that orbit (go around) the sun. Studies show that there may be gold on asteroids.

BCE meaning "before the common era". When this appears after a date, it refers to the time before the Christian religion began. BCE dates are always counted backwards.

CE meaning "common era". When this appears after a date, it refers to the time after the Christian religion began.

dam barrier to hold back the flow of water. Dams help prevent flooding.

element substance that cannot be separated into simpler substances by chemical means. Gold is an element known as Au.

expedition journey for a particular purpose. Pizarro set out on an expedition to find gold in Peru.

laser instrument that uses light to help doctors perform some kinds of surgery. Gold coating helps lasers work better during surgery.

legend story handed down from earlier times that may or may not be true. There are many legends about lost gold.

lode mining underground mining for gold, also called vein mining. Lode mines may extend underground for many kilometres.

mine pit or tunnel from which minerals (such as coal, gold, or diamonds) are taken; also, to dig a mine, to obtain something from a mine, or to work in a mine. The world's deepest gold mine is in South Africa.

miner someone who works in a mine. Some miners work deep inside the earth.

mineral substance obtained by mining, such as an ore. Gold is often found with minerals such as lead or copper.

monarch king or queen

open pit mine surface mine in which earth is removed layer by layer to reveal minerals. Miners remove trees to create open pit mines.

ore metal-bearing mineral or rock that can be mined at a profit. Ore sometimes contains gold.

pharaoh ruler in ancient Egypt. In Egypt, the pharaohs owned all the gold.

placer mining method of finding gold that has washed into rivers and streams. U-shaped boxes called rockers are used in placer mining.

proverb short, well-known saying containing a wise thought. There are many proverbs about gold.

Find out more

Books

Gold, Ron Edwards and James Gladstone (Crabtree, 2004)

How to Get Rich in the California Gold Rush, Tod Olson (National Geographic, 2008)

Tutankhamun, Gill Harvey (Usborne, 2006)

Websites

Learn about the California Gold Rush.
http://pbskids.org/wayback/goldrush/index.html

Explore Tutankhamen's riches.
www.nationalgeographic.com/ngkids/0508/

Places to visit

Visit a jewellery shop and see real gold jewellery.

Dolaucothi Gold Mines
Pumsaint
Llanwrda
Carmarthanshire SA19 8US
www.nationaltrust.org.uk/main/w-dolaucothigoldmines

Visit a Roman gold mine and try panning for gold.

Index